The Bully Met My Dad!

. . .and Became My Friend

By Patrice Lee

Illustrated by Francesco Paolo Ardizzone

The Bully Met My Dad . . .and Became My Friend
Copyright 2014

Published by Leep4Joy Books, a Division of Feinstein Development & Associates
Printed in the United States of America

Library of Congress Catalog-in-Publication Data
ISBN: # 978-0-9837207-9-9

Edited by: Cathryn Williams
Cover Art: Francesco Paolo Ardizzone
Page Layout: Bob Ivory Jr., Ivory Coast Media

Please send all correspondence to:

Feinstein Development and Associates, P.O. Box 48172, Oak Park, MI 48237

Just Like You!

Our neighborhood - our city, is a better town.
Everything's better, Dad, when you're around.
It's because of the wonderful things you do,
That when I grow up, I want to be -
Just like you!

Thank you for loving me, unconditionally.
Yes, Dad, you're who I'd like to be.

"Adore God. Reverence and cherish your parents. Love your neighbor as yourself . . ."
Thomas Jefferson

Introduction

Benjamin is an eight year old boy, who is very talented in baseball. He is so talented, that everyone in the neighborhood and all of the children at school know him.

The problem occurs when Benjamin gets noticed by one who is a bully, who's not so happy about all of the attention Benjamin has been getting. Although the two boys are about the same age, the bully is slightly larger. And one day, he decides to attack.

The theme of *The Bully Met My Dad!* centers around a father's ability to look beyond the bad actions committed against his son, and show love. See how love goes beyond disappointment, hurt and pain to help two boys become friends.

Expect only good things to happen, when you love your neighbor(s) as you love yourself. Let's read and see what happens to the two boys, when Benjamin's dad intervenes.

"Be kinder than necessary, for everyone you meet is fighting some kind of battle . . ."
J. M. Barrie

Everywhere he went he took his bat and ball,
For Benjamin loved every sport,
And wanted to do them all.

But, as he played each sport, he knew in his heart,
That baseball was his first choice.
He'd loved it from the start.

He continued to practice, and to pursue his interest;
He practiced until he became so much
Better than all the rest.

In fact, Benjamin became so good,
You could hear his name echo
In the halls at school and
Throughout the neighborhood.

One day, just as he finished playing ball,
A boy much bigger than he,
Shoved him from behind
And knocked him to his knee.

Benjamin pulled himself up,
And as he wiped his face,
He proceeded to run home to a safer place.

This place, you will see,
Is a great big garage,
Where he and his Dad spend time
Together and work on cars.

The bully followed close behind.
The boy's Dad spotted him right away.
He called out to the bully,
"It's alright. You can stay."

For what this Dad saw
Was a very lonely child,
One who'd been neglected
For quite a little while.

He saw his tattered clothes.
He noticed the dirt.
He saw that his aggressive
Expression had exceeded the hurt.

He knew the boy needed
A chance to experience life
Without the strong expression of anger thru strife.

In a very few words the dad shared his thoughts.
And, in a sentence or two,
A lesson was taught.

Suddenly, the bully knew
He was in the right place,
You could see it from the change
In expressions on his face,

For it was this Dad's decision
To set an example for his son,
That with his kind reception,
Even the bully could learn to relax and have fun.

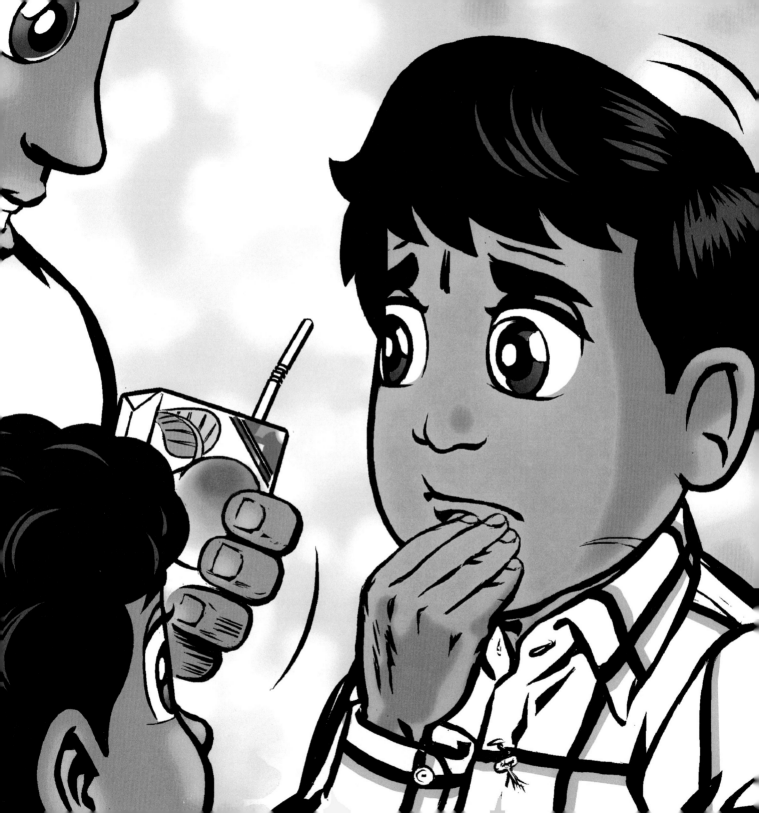

With his tearful reaction,
As the Dad extended his hand,
The bully knew in his heart,
He had just met a friend.

Today, the boys look out for each other.
They're kind to others too.
These two boys respect authority!
And both do well in school.

And, if you happen to notice them on any given day,
You'll see they've become best of friends,
Both at school and at play.

Now, they play baseball together, and have formed a little team.
But, the Major Leagues for the one named Benjamin
Will be more than just a dream.

My Dad Is Your Friend Too!

The bully is a person, who's not so bad - after all.
He may have experienced great disappointment,
Or maybe he's had a bad break;
He could be in a lot of pain or someone whose heart aches.

If you'll show a little kindness, things are gonna' be okay;
Just look for tomorrow to be a better day.
And you'll see in the end,
That this little bully just needed a friend.

Thank you Dad, for being a friend!

"Let brotherly love continue" (Hebrews 13:1).

A Child's Meaningful Prayer:

Dear God,

Please cleanse my heart, mind and soul.
Save me now, and make me whole.
I believe Jesus died for me, so I will not fear.
For I know in my heart, Lord, You are always near.
      In Jesus' Name. Amen.

"Fret not thyself because of evildoers. . ." (Psalm 37:1a).

"Bible Verses" to Keep Children Strong When They Feel Weak

~

"For God has not given us the spirit of fear; but of power, and of love and of a sound mind" (2 Timothy 1:7).

"In Your presence is fullness of joy. . ." (Psalm 16:11NKJV).

"The Lord is my refuge and strength, a very present help in trouble" (Psalm 46:1).

"The Lord is on my side. I will not fear. . ." (Psalm 118:6).

". . .greater is He that is in you (me), than he that is in the world" (1 John 4:4).

". . .Vengeance is mine saith the Lord, I will repay" (Romans 12:19b).

"Love one another." (John 13:34a) for "There is no fear in love" (1 John 4:18a).

". . .let us love one another: for love is of God. . ." (1 John 4:7).

(Bible verses taken from the King James Version, unless specified.)

~ Love forgives and remembers no wrong ~

The Lesson Learned:

When Benjamin is attacked by a bully, his Dad reacts with an unusual response. He looks beyond the attack and observes that the bully needs "love."

The Bully Met My Dad clearly shows how a father's demonstration of love can make a big difference in the life of his immediate family, as well as in the lives of other children in his community. The "bully" is a brand new person now, who smiles, shares and has become a real friend.

After all. . .all he needed was a friend.

Other Lessons Learned:

1. Moms and Dads are responsible for training and teaching their children. Good training leads to a brighter future for each child. "Train up a child in the way he should go, and when he is old, he will **not depart** from it" (Proverbs 22:6).

2. Benjamin's dad demonstrates love through his actions. He chooses to love the bully with **unconditional love**. When love is present, fear goes away. "There's no fear in love. . .perfect love **casts out** fear" (1 John 4:18a)

3. Benjamin's dad is a peacemaker. He **pursues** peace. Peace keeps your heart and mind healthy. It **surpasses** all understanding. "When a man's ways please the Lord, He makes even his enemies to be at peace with him" (Proverbs 16:7).

4. It is easy to love your neighbor, if you love yourself, even if your neighbor seems to be unlovable at times. Keep walking in a loving way, and things will **improve.** That's what Benjamin's dad does. He forgives the bully and extends kindness. Love is evident in his actions – words, deeds and tone of voice. "...thou shalt love thy neighbor as thyself" (Matthew 22:39b).

Words Defined:

cast out - get rid of; to remove.

improve - turn around in a positive way, change for the better

not depart - will not stray away from, will not leave, will stick with what he knows, will eventually come back to what he was taught;

pursue(s) - go after, seek(s), looks for a way to have something

surpasses – go beyond the expected norm, beyond the imagination; is greater than.

"unconditional love" – to love without limitation; without limits

Talking points: (Gr. 1-3. Have children fill in the blanks. Underlined words can be left blank.)

Have discussion about Benjamin's "safe place." The _____ is a place where this father gets things done. From car maintenance to bike repair, if it is something mechanical or technical, this Dad can do it. The garage is also a place where father and son can sit and talk about _____ or just relax. It is their special place. It is where _____ feels safe.

Review Questions:

1. What does Benjamin do well?
2. Why was Benjamin so popular?
3. Was everyone happy for him?
4. After Benjamin hit the home run, what happened?
5. What was his reaction?   Who did he tell about the bully?
6. How did Benjamin's Dad respond/react when he saw that the bully had followed Benjamin home out of curiosity?
7. How do you think the little boy (Benjamin) felt when the bully followed him?
   a. puzzled   b. confused   c. concerned   d. all of the above
8. a. The bully seemed/appeared to be troubled.   ____ True   ____ False
   b. His posture suggests that he was very unhappy. ____ True ____ False
   c. The bully's clothes appeared to be tattered or torn. ____ True ____ False
9. The bully's clothes were too small for him. ____ True ____ False
10. The bully's attitude improved after Benjamin's Dad talked with him.   ____ True ____ False
11. What did Benjamin's family give the bully?   a. water   b. juice box
12. How did Benjamin's Dad end the conversation?
13. What affect did the conversation have on the bully and Benjamin?
14. Now that they are friends, name at least three positive things that the boys do.
15. Name five things you can do to help stop the bullying in your school, neighborhood or community.

Talking Points:

Answers: a. garage   b. anything   c. Benjamin

Review Questions:
(Answers)

1. Plays baseball.
2. He was an exceptional ball player.
3. No.
4. He was attacked by a bully, who knocked him down to his knees.
5. He ran home. He told his dad.
6. He beckoned the bully to come to him.
7. d. all of the above
8. a. True   b. True   c. True
9. False
10. True
11. b. juice box
12. with a handshake
13. They became very good friends.
14. This answer will open up a platform for discussion
15. Maybe these positive suggestions can be used in your community. It is important that dads be involved.

Made in the USA
San Bernardino, CA
08 May 2017